The Third Whirligig

Written by Paul Shipton

Illustrated by Sarah Horne

There were three whirligig bugs on top
of a pond.
The first bug was hungry. So was the
second bug. But the third bug was afraid.

It is a bit early to search for food.
There may be birds. They will eat us.

Do not be silly!
There are no birds.

The first whirligig began to glide across
the pond to search for food.
The next bug went after him.

They did not see the shadow on the pond.
It was a bird ... a big, HUNGRY bird!

The bird saw the whirligigs on top of the pond and said "YUM!"

The first and second whirligigs did not see the bird. Only the third whirligig saw it.

"Oh no!" the third bug said to herself.
She began to whirl and whirl on top
of the water.

Under the water a fish saw all the whirling ... a big, HUNGRY fish! It swam to the top of the pond.

The bird flew down.
It was near the water ...

The fish swam up.
It was near the top of the pond ...

BOOM!
The fish hit the bird and
the bird hit the fish.

The bird flew off.
The fish swam back to the dark waters.

The first whirligig was happy.
So was the second whirligig.
"Thanks!" they said to the third whirligig.

Then they began to glide off.
"What are you doing?" asked the
third whirligig.
"Searching for food!" they told her.

"There must be thirty birds in the sky," said the third whirligig.
"Some bugs never learn."